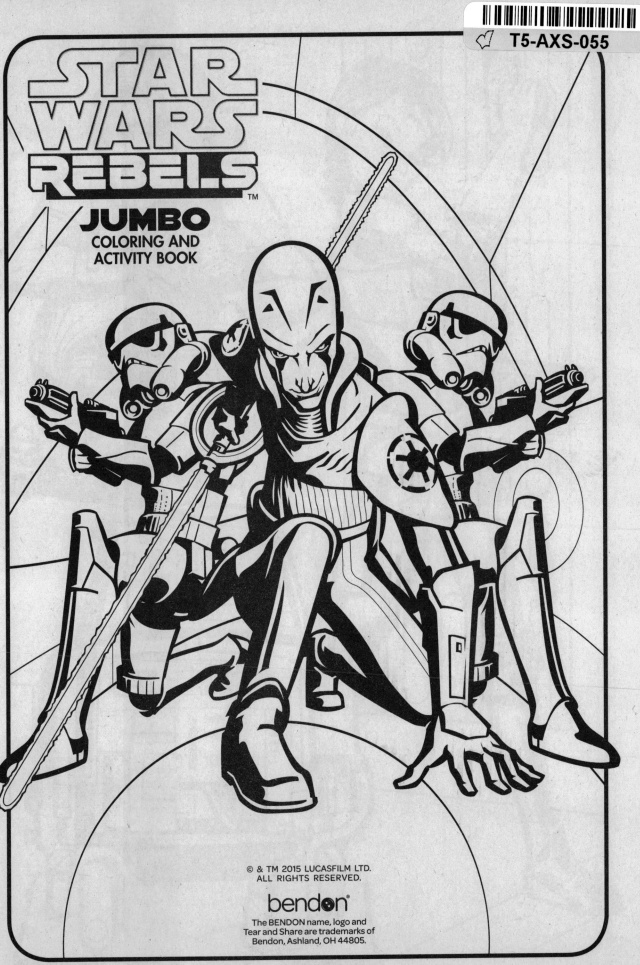

STAR WARS REBELS™

JUMBO
COLORING AND ACTIVITY BOOK

bendon®

The BENDON name, logo and
Tear and Share are trademarks of
Bendon, Ashland, OH 44805.

SPOT THE DIFFERENCE

Which Kanan is different?

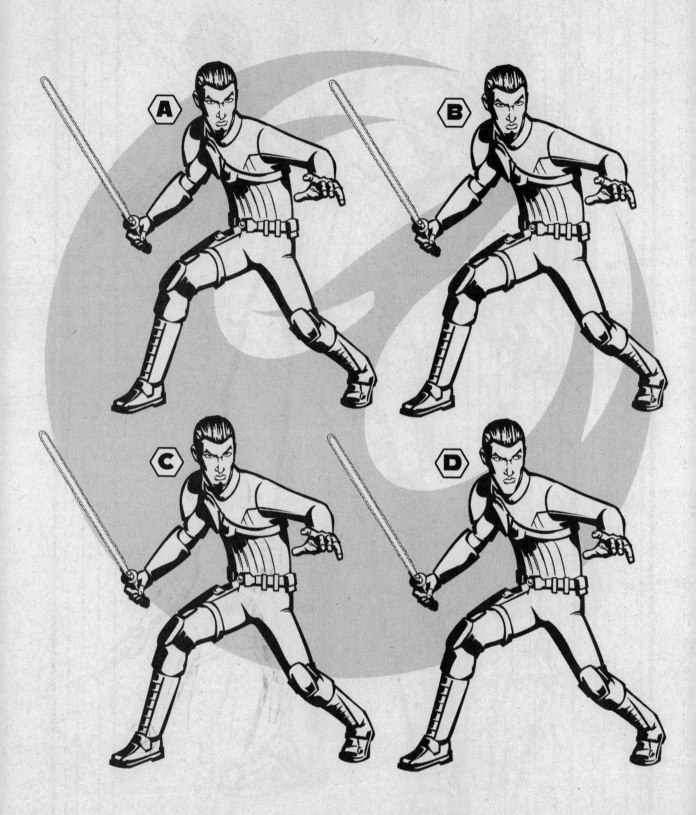

ANSWER: D

SPOT THE DIFFERENCE

Which Sabine is different?

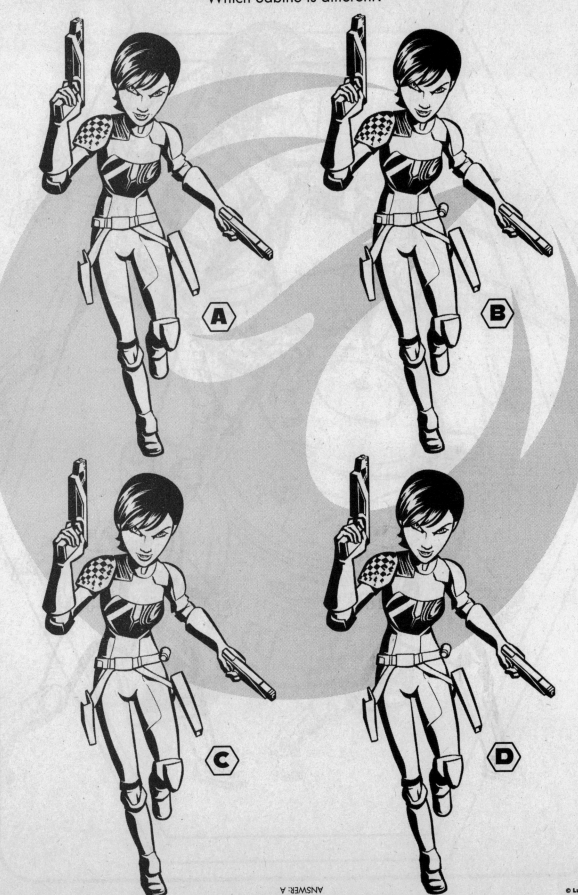

SHIP-SHAPE

Draw lines to match each ship to its shape.

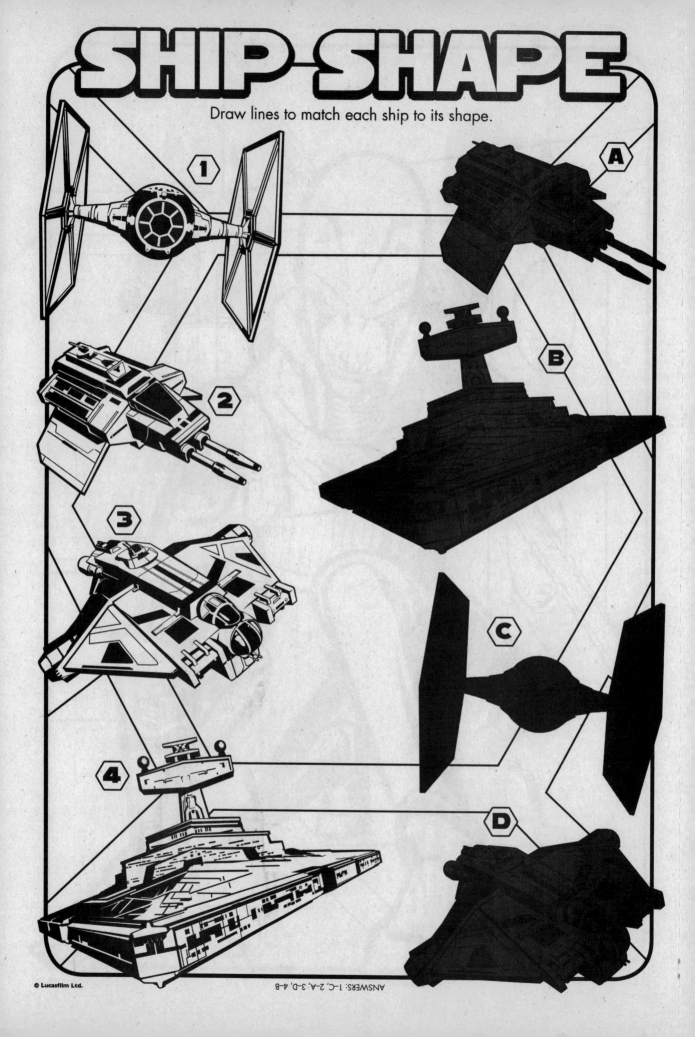

ANSWERS: 1-C, 2-A, 3-D, 4-B

SPOT THE DIFFERENCE

Which Ezra and Chopper are different?

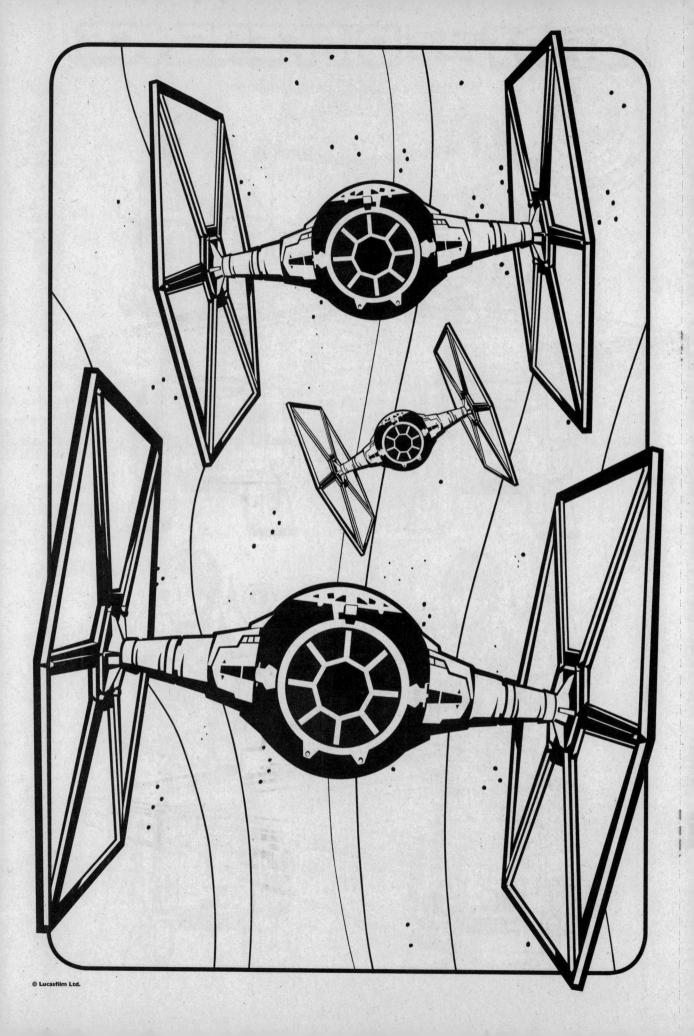

© Lucasfilm Ltd.

GHOST

Get Ready, Get Set...
DRAW!

Imperial Stormtroopers have been deployed.
Draw the other half of the stormtrooper.

TIE FIGHTERS

The swift, maneuverable Twin Ion Engine Fighters enforce the Imperial rule
of the Galactic Empire. Draw the other half of this TIE Fighter.

DEPLOY THE TROOPS

Number the forces. How many stormtroopers do you count?

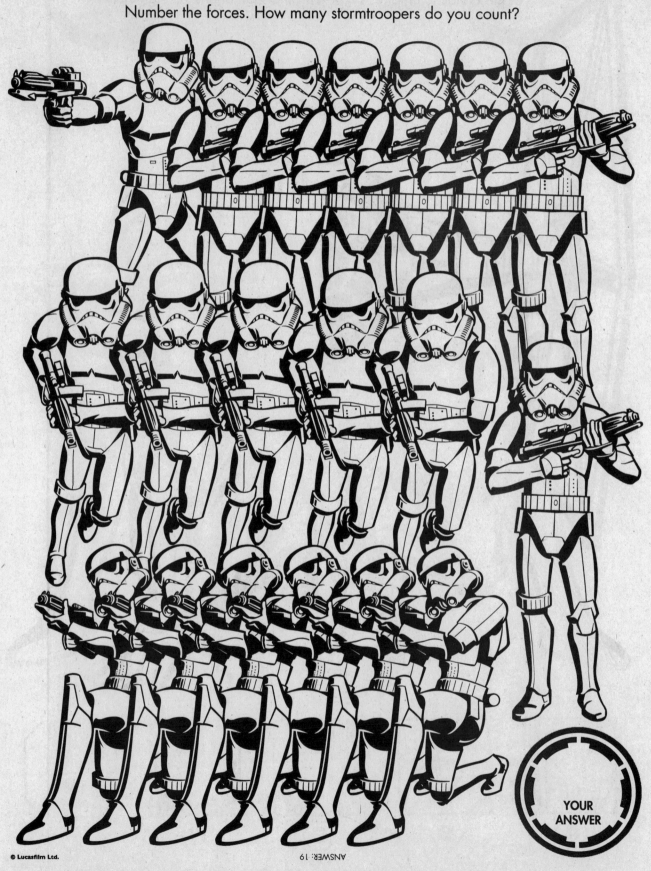

YOUR
ANSWER

ANSWER: 19

THE INQUISITOR

Which square completes the drawing?

A   B   C   D

YOUR ANSWER

ANSWER: B

© Lucasfilm Ltd.

INQUISITOR

SPOT THE DIFFERENCE

Which Inquisitor is different?

ANSWER: A

SPOT THE DIFFERENCE

Which Zeb is different?

A

B

C

D

ANSWER: C

MAKE WORDS FROM THE LETTERS IN

Sabine Wren

MAKE WORDS FROM THE LETTERS IN

Hera Syndulla

_____   _____

_____   _____

_____   _____

_____   _____

_____   _____

_____   _____

© Lucasfilm Ltd.

FINISH HIM!

DRAW THE
OTHER HALF
OF THE
INQUISITOR.

© Lucasfilm Ltd.

© Lucasfilm Ltd.

MAKE WORDS FROM THE LETTERS IN
Garazeb Orrelios

_____   _____

_____   _____

_____   _____

_____   _____

_____   _____

_____   _____

_____   _____

REBEL
WORD SEARCH

```
B H S Y N D U L L A L
R E L K E L I W T M I N
I R Z J S T A R W O G
D A J R K E W A R S H
G L A S A B I N E O T R
E E R I N R S F S S S R
R S R J A R R T S L A E
U A U T N A M U H E B L
V T S B W R E N G B E I
A C H O P P E R W E R O
P H A N T O M C D R E S
D I O R D G A R A Z E B
```

STAR   EZRA   HUMAN
WARS   KANAN   TWI'LEK
REBELS   HERA   LESAT
GHOST   SABINE   DROID
PHANTOM   ZEB   LIGHTSABER
      CHOPPER

IMPERIAL FORCE
WORD SEARCH

```
S R E B A S T H G I L A
B T V W Y F O G A H S E
M I O D E S T R O Y E R
L E U R L A I R E P M I
C D I E M F S L E B E R
G A L A C T I C G K E F
Q R V B I N R H T S M I
V T A R D S T O L I P G
A H D T I Q J T O E I H
O P E R S B E L S P R T
Z S R E C I F F O C E E
L M I N Q U I S I T O R
```

STORMTROOPER

GALACTIC   STAR   LIGHTSABER

EMPIRE   DESTROYER   DARTH

TIE   IMPERIAL   VADER

FIGHTER   OFFICERS

PILOTS   INQUISITOR

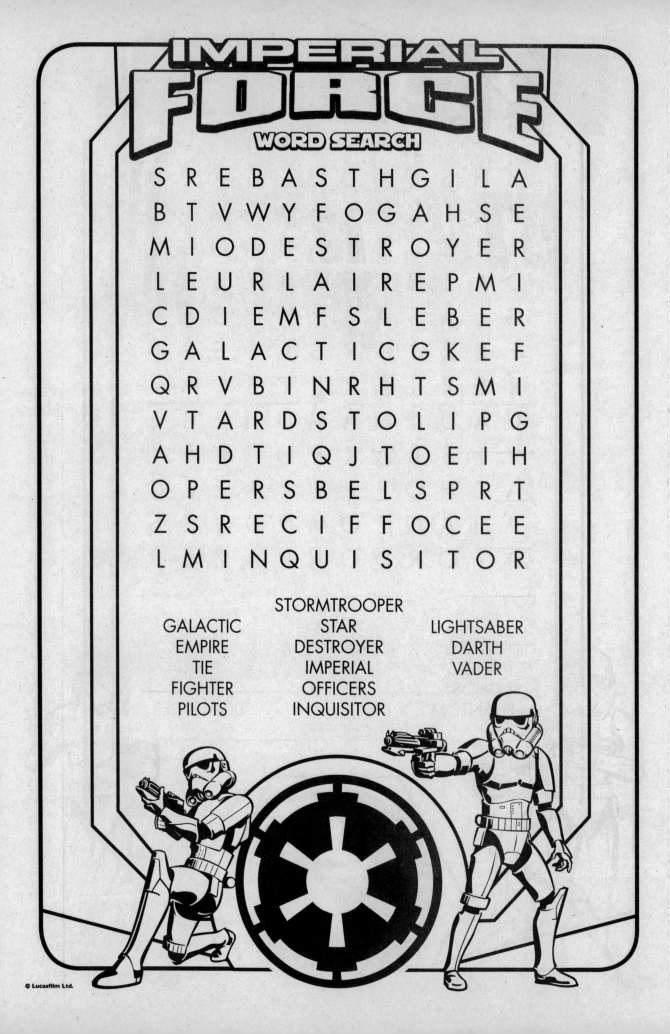

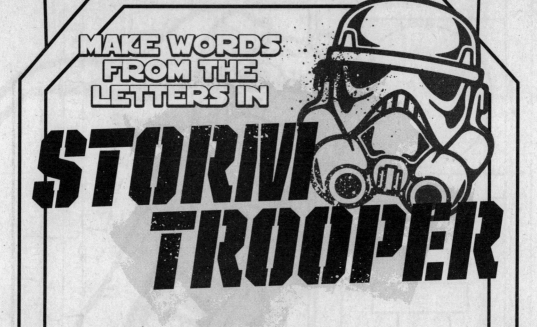

MAKE WORDS FROM THE LETTERS IN

STORM TROOPER

_____   _____

_____   _____

_____   _____

_____   _____

_____   _____

_____   _____

_____   _____

C1-1OP

© Lucasfilm Ltd.

CHOPPED IN HALF

Chopper has been put together from many parts. Draw the other half of the rebels' droid.

IMPERIAL SHADOWS

Draw lines to match each stormtrooper with its shadow.

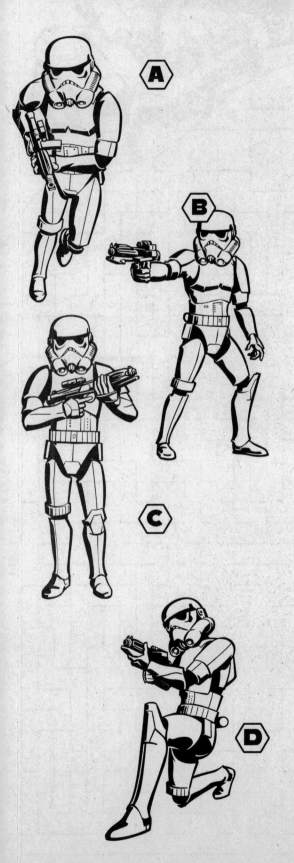

Make your way through the maze.
Watch out for stormtroopers!

BLAST THEM!

START

FINISH

© Lucasfilm Ltd.

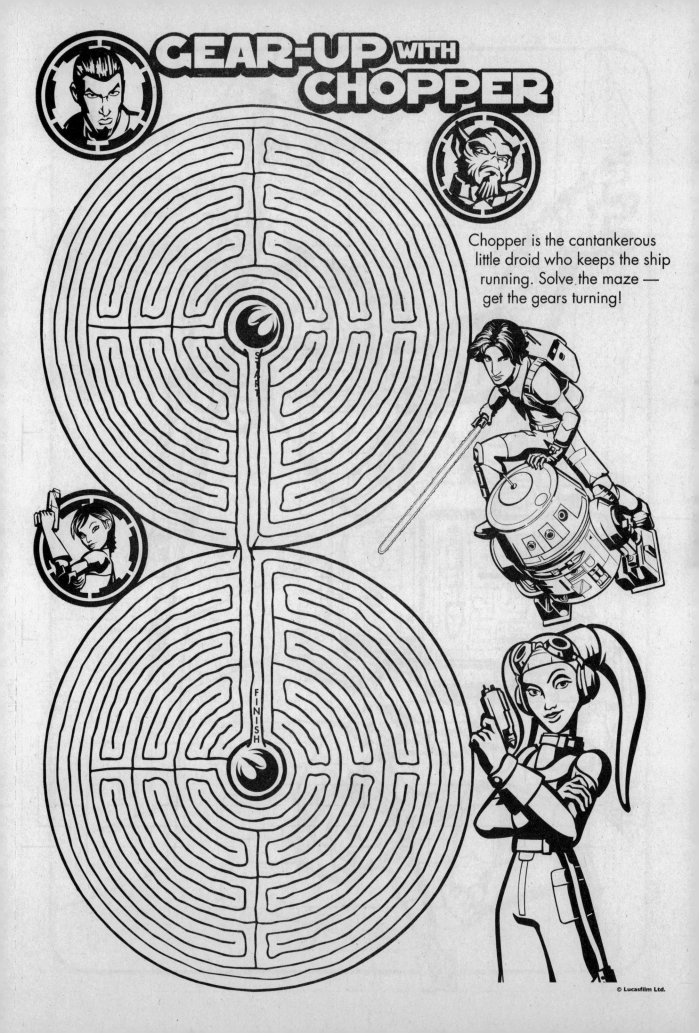

GEAR-UP WITH CHOPPER

Chopper is the cantankerous little droid who keeps the ship running. Solve the maze — get the gears turning!

START

FINISH

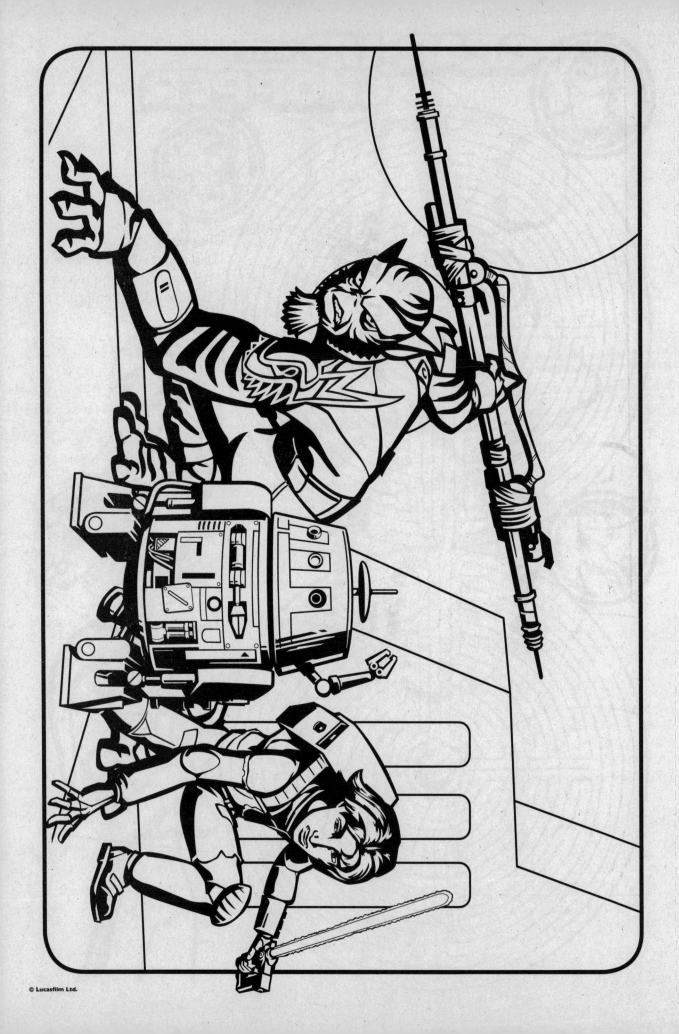

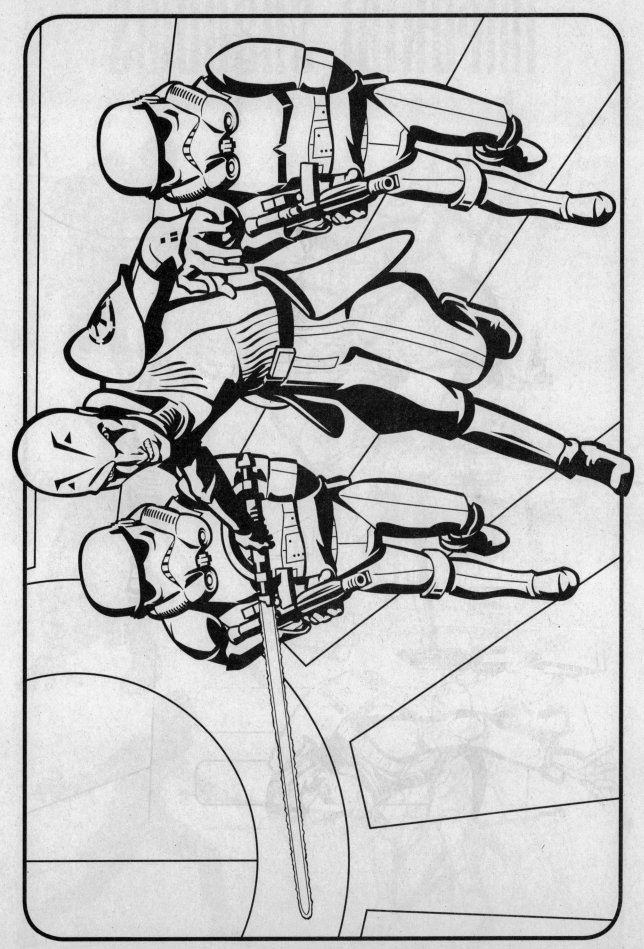

IMPERIAL SHADOWS

Draw lines to match the Inquisitor with his correct shadow.

ANSWERS: 1-C, 2-A, 3-B

© Lucasfilm Ltd.

AMAZING MANEUVERS

Help the rebels escape the grasp of the Inquisitor!

START

FINISH

FIND YOUR DESTINY

Follow the path that brings together a Jedi and his apprentice.

START

FINISH

© Lucasfilm Ltd.